The Giving Tree:
A Retelling of a Traditional Métis Story about Giving and Receiving

Laarbr Kawmaekit:
Aen kiitwam achimook
Aen histwayr chi maykik pi aen ootistikook

Written and Illustrated by Leah Dorion
Michif Translation by Norman Fleury

Library and Archives Canada Cataloguing in Publication

Dorion, Leah, 1970-
The giving tree: a retelling of a traditional Métis story / Leah Dorion; Norman Fleury, translator.

Accompanied by a CD.
Text and CD narration in English and Michif.
ISBN 978-0-920915-90-5

1. **Métis--Folklore--Juvenile literature. I. Fleury, Norman II. Gabriel Dumont Institute of Native Studies and Applied Research III. Title.**

PS8557.O7483G59 2009   **j398.2089'970712**   **C2009-905502-3**

Gabriel Dumont Institute Project Team:

Darren R. Préfontaine, Project Leader and Editor
David Morin, Graphic Designer, Editor
Meredith Penner, Graphic Designer
Amaranta Sokol, Editor
Karon Shmon, Publishing Coordinator
Globe Printers, Saskatoon, Printer

The Gabriel Dumont Institute
2—604 22nd Street West
Saskatoon, SK S7M 5W1
www.gdins.org
www.metismuseum.ca

The Gabriel Dumont Institute acknowledges the financial support of the Office of the Federal Interlocutor for Métis and Non-Status Indians, Indian and Northern Affairs Canada for the production and publishing of this resource.

Canadä

The Giving Tree:
A Retelling of a Traditional Métis Story about Giving and Receiving

Laarbr Kawmaekit:
Aen kiitwam achimook
Aen histwayr chi maykik pi aen ootistikook

Dedicated to Frank Tomkins, a respected Métis Elder,
and to my son Louis (Richard) Lafferty.

A long time ago there was once a tree. It was an old twisted Manitoba maple.

Kayaash il avait aen naarbr. Sitae aen vyeu araab di Manitoba tapishkoot aen kii washakanith.

This Manitoba maple was special as she had a large weathered hollow within her trunk. Maybe this hollow was once home to a family of birds or it might have been the sleeping place for a travelling porcupine.

Laraab di Manitoba kii kishchiitaytakoshiw pi kayaash ooshchi kii wiipishiw daan sa shoosh. Maashkoot lii pchi twaezoo akoota kii wiikiwuk maashkoot miina lii portipik kii nanipawuk.

One thing for certain, this tree was beloved by my grandpa. Grandpa often called her the "giving tree."

Poor saartaen ni mooshoom onhi laarbr kii kishchiitaymew. Ni mooshoom mishchaetwow kii shinikatew "laarbr kawmaekit."

So I asked my grandpa to tell me a story from his childhood memories. He said:

Gii kakwaechimow ni mooshoom chi wiitamowit aen nistwayr ka ishi pay kishkishitt ashpinae ka apishishshitt. Kii itwew:

"Long ago, when I was a little boy, my mama and papa often travelled by horse and wagon to visit our relations."

"Kayaash maana ka ayapishshiyaan ni mama pi ni papa ki pa kiwikawaewuk nutr paraantii avik lii zhvoo an waagoon."

"My favourite part of our trip was the pipe break at the giving tree. This tree was located at the half-way point between our related Métis villages."

"Iita nawut ka myeutaman en wayaezh ka ayayak ka nakiiyak chi piitwak aara laarbr kawmaekit. Laarbr ahaara kii apiw iita lii Michif ka wiikichik."

"It was the 'Métis way' to stop for tea and bannock at the giving tree."

"Aykooshi lii Michif ka tootakihk aen nakiichik aara laarbr kawmaekit poor li tii pi la gaalet."

"As small kids we got very excited at the sight of the tree as she appeared around the bend in the trail."

"Ka apishishiyak gii chiikaytaenaan ka taepapimayak laarbr iita ooshchi li shmaen ka washakamook."

"It was our tradition to sprinkle an offering of tobacco at the base of her trunk every time we visited the tree."

"Gii piiwayhanaan li tabaa an ba la shoosch ka kiiwkawayak laarbr."

"It was fun to unload our wagon for a friendly family picnic under her protective canopy."

"Gii moochikitanaan aen niitinashooyak aen chiikaytamak daan nutr picnic avik nutr famii ita ka kawashtek."

"We loved to make a small fire to boil our tea, cook our bannock, gather around to tell stories, and to chew on our dry meat."

"Gii miyeuytaenaan aen pchi feu aen ooshitayak chi ooshamak nutr tii, chi kiishishwayak nutr gaalett, chi mamoyapiyak lii zistwayr chi achimooyak, pi chi mamakwatamak nutr vyaand shaysh."

"The most magical memory that I have was the time when my mama forgot to pack our sugar into the grub box."

"Mitoni aen kishkishiyaan enn fway mama ka waniikayt soon suk chi li paktiit daan la bwayt di maangii."

"'Oh my goodness gracious,' said mama, 'I forgot to pack sugar for our tea and bannock!'"

"'Kiishinatakamihk,' itwew mama, 'gii waniikaan chi li paktiyaan li suk poor nutr tii pi la gaalett.'"

"'Son,' spoke papa, 'Come here, I want you to help me with something.' So papa lifted me up to look into the big hollow within the maple tree."

"'Mon pchi gaarsoon' itwew papa, 'ashtum oota ki nidwaymitin chi paywichihiyenn.' Aykooshi papa gii oopinik chi piitikwaytapiyaan ita ka wiipishik laarbr."

"To my surprise in the bottom of the hollow there was sugar, tea, bundles of tobacco, letters, flour, and even a pair of moccasins. There was so much stuff hidden deep inside her hollow."

"Gii kooshkwayten daan li foon di laarbr akoota li suk, li tii, lii paaktoon di tabaw, li lettr, la faarinn pi ahpo miina enn perr di sooyii moo. Mishchet kii kachikatew kakiiyow kaykway iita laarbr ka wiipishik."

"I was awestruck, as I pulled out a little canister of sugar."

"Mitoni gii kooshkwapishininn aen oochipitamann enn pchit kan di suk."

"As papa lowered me down I said, 'Papa, what's all that stuff doing in there?' My papa explained to me that this giving tree is a sacred place for us Métis people."

"An baw papa aen pakitinit ditwaan, 'Papa tanayki kakiyow anihi li maanzhii akoota ka aashtayk?' Papa mitooni gii wiitamak ita awa laarbr kawmaekit mitooni kishchiitaytakwun."

"He told me that for generations the tree hollow was used by Métis travellers as a cache, so that it could help our people out in times of need."

"Gii wiitamak ashpinais kaayash ooshchi laarbr ka wiipishitt lii Michif kii apachihaywuk chi kachikayk chi wiichihachik awiya ka nootaypayit kaykway."

"My papa said that it was the 'Métis way' to use the tree cache as a message centre and as an emergency supply stash."

"Papa kii itwew 'aykooshi lii Michif' ka ishchikaychik kaayash, laarbr ki apachihaewuk chi wiitamakayk kaykway pi miina ka kishchi manayshik kaykway."

"For generations the tree cache was a symbol of honesty and respect."

"Kayaash ooshchi laarbr kawmaekit kii ooschi kanwapimikashoo tapishkoot kwayesh aen tootamik pi miina chi kishchiitaymook."

"Papa told me that once a young man left an engagement ring for his sweetheart inside the tree."

"Papa gii wiitamak enn fway aen nomm soon zhoon avaan chi wiiwit aen kii nakatat didaan laarbr."

"Two days later, the ring was delivered to his sweetheart safely by a man passing by her home."

"Deu zhoor apray, aen nomm aen pimotayt aara sa zhaang sa mayzoon iyew kii pay miyiko soon zhoon."

"Papa loved our old Métis ways."

"Papa kii kischi shahkitow taanshi lii vyeu Michif ka kii ishipimatishichik kaayash."

"Papa spoke of our beliefs:
'if you take something from
the tree cache you are
responsible to put something
back in return.'"

"Papa kii taashitum ka pay
ishi: 'tapwaytamuk kiishpin
kaykway ka ootinamun
sa praan chi kiitwam
ashtayenn.'"

"Papa reminded me that it is our Métis way to be kind, generous, and helpful to others."

"Taapitow Papa gii kishkishomik niiyanaan lii Michif ni kitimakaymanaan ayishiinew, noo ki shashakishinaan pi ki nita wiichiiwanaan."

"Mama came over to the tree to get the sugar canister. She put several folded polka-dotted hankies and a small pail into my hand so I could offer them back into the hollow."

"Mama kii pay natum la kaan di suk daan laarbr ooshchi. Gii miiyik mishchet lii pchi mooshwayr pi enn pchit shayayr chi kiitwam ashtayaan daan laarbr."

"Mama thought that somebody might find the hankies useful especially if they had a runny nose or needed a rag."

"Mama kii itaytum awiyuk chi apachihayit lii mooshwayr soortoo poor leu nii obaendoon poor aen laenge."

"It was so fun to place our offering back into the maple tree. I wondered who would someday get those polka-dotted hankies."

"Gii chiikaytenn aen kiitwum maekiyaan daan laraab. Awana chi mishkawut gii tayteen oonhi lii mooshwayr."

"That day I understood why the old timers called her the 'giving tree' as she stood for everything good that we Métis people believed in."

"Laa gii kiskaytenn tanayki lii vyeu ka shnikatachik 'laarbr kawmaekit.' Kii wiitamakew kakiyow lii Michif ka ishi tapwaetakik."

As grandpa finished his story he smiled, winked, and made me promise to one day tell my own children the story of the 'giving tree.'

Ka poonachimoot soon nistwayr ni mooshoom papinakoshew pi miina chiipiikwayiiw, pi miina chi ashotamun gootik chi achimooshtawakik mii zaanfaan oma listwayr 'laarbr kawmaekit.'

He said, "Tell our stories so future generations will remember about the true spirit of being Métis!"

Itwew, "achimook nutr zistwayr ayka wiikat nutr zaanfan chi waaniikaychik awana aen vray Michif!"

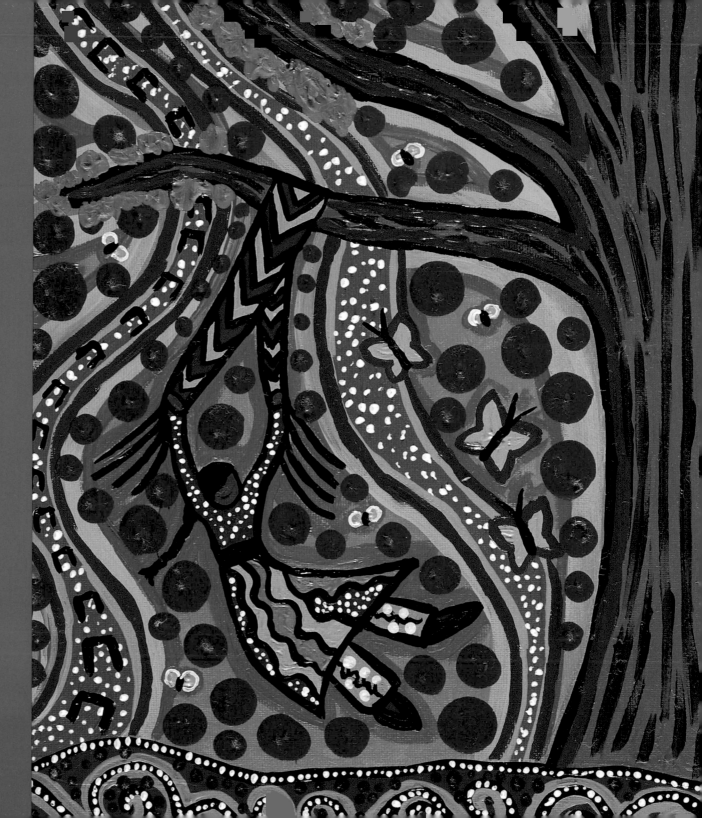

Many old-time Métis values are still in existence within the contemporary Métis community. One need not look far to see these traditional beliefs embedded in the root of contemporary Métis families. However, we need to go back and think about these old Métis ways so we can continue to pass on these traditions to the next generation of Métis children. We need to consciously talk to our children about our values so that they will remain at the core of who we are as Métis people.

Creator (Li Boon Jeu): The Métis have always encouraged a daily relationship with the Creator. The expression of gratitude for all of the Creator's wondrous gifts was a significant aspect of the Métis way. A loving, generous, kind Creator was the source of inspiration for daily living.

Honesty (Kwayesh chi totamik): Traditionally, Métis people highly valued honesty. Parents were taught to serve as role models for honest behaviour. Other peoples' boundaries and possessions were always respected. Stealing was a rare offence in Métis communities, and if it happened there were very serious consequences.

Respect (Kishchiitaytamik): Respect was integrated into all areas of life. Respect for the Creator, Mother Earth, the living world, and oneself was paramount towards living in a good Métis way.

Love (Shaakihiwayhk): An open loving heart was highly valued in the traditional Métis way of life. Developing unconditional love for yourself, your family, community, nation, and for all of creation was important in order to create a healthy Métis community. Serving as role models and teachers, Elders taught how to live in a loving way to their grandchildren. The grandchildren would then know who they were and where they came from.

Sharing (Taashkinikayen): In the Métis way, sharing your gifts and abundance with others was a vital part of living. Children were taught to give from the heart without reservation. It was believed that the more you gave from the heart the more you will receive. It was understood that when you gave in a good way, the good came back to you fourfold. To reinforce generosity, Métis people were taught to give away even their most treasured possessions. Giveaways were a reminder that the material world is only one aspect of the greater vision.

Caring (Pishkaymitook): In the Métis way, caring for yourself and others was expected. Helping care for others who could not look after themselves was practiced by everybody in the Métis community. Métis hunters made sure that the Elders always had enough meat and provisions. Able children were encouraged to spend time with Elders and help them with small tasks such as writing letters, cooking, or making tea.

Courage (Kooraazh): Métis people were taught to take risks for the betterment of themselves and others. In the Métis way, having courage against injustice and giving your honest opinion was highly valued. Standing up for yourself, your values, and your beliefs was encouraged.

Balance (Balaans): One of the sacred laws in the traditional Métis worldview was the Great Law of Harmony and Balance. According to this Métis law, an individual must place an offering before they took something. Often, a prayer or tobacco offering was made before harvesting animals, plants, and other resources from the land in order to maintain balance in creation. Living in balance mentally, emotionally, physically, and spiritually was stressed.

Mother Earth (Ni maamaa la tayr): Great levels of reverence and respect for Mother Earth were practiced by the Métis. Honouring the land and all the gifts that she provided was a key aspect of Métis culture and society. Treating earth as a living, "motherly" entity was taught to children at a young age. Children were encouraged to talk to the Earth Mother and acknowledge her in their prayers.

Patience (Pa iksitii): Taking time to enjoy the processes of life was a common Métis tradition. Learning to look, listen, and learn was a highly valued skill. Taking time to think before acting and using prayer before making important decisions was a common aspect of the Métis way. Doing things carefully, mindfully, and purposefully the first time was encouraged. Métis carpenters always said, "measure twice—cut once."

Strength (La fors): It was believed by the Métis that it took a warrior's strength to develop a person's gifts. It was the role of Métis Elders to help youth find their own special gifts and higher purpose in life. Healthy competition, hard work, dedication, and persistence were valued by the Métis. Personal fortitude was purposefully developed so that the Métis could adapt and respond to life's ever changing circumstances.

Kindness (Kitimakaymiwek): All acts of kindness were acknowledged, supported, and celebrated by the Métis community. Children were always taught to be kind to strangers and to give them their best hospitality. Kindness was a significant part of the Métis way. All children were taught to be kind to animals, strangers, and to the vulnerable and less fortunate.

Tolerance (Aanjeurii): Being non-judgmental of others was highly valued by the Métis community. Learning how to debate and discuss matters with others in a good way was always fun and exciting. Children were encouraged to be critical thinkers and to question the world around them for the betterment of themselves and the rest of the community. Searching out other peoples' opinions and point of view was a practice encouraged by Métis Elders. Learning to agree to disagree was an important Métis tradition.

Three-Fold Métis Decision-Making Model

Past   **Present**   **FUTURE**

Our Métis infinity flag represents the Sacred Law of Harmony and Balance. The Métis infinity flag was flown to remind the Métis community about their responsibility to look concurrently at the past, present, and future. The infinity symbol reminds Métis people to find the balance between our First Nations and European heritages. Furthermore, the infinity symbol teaches us how to create Harmony and Balance in all our decisions. For generations, the Métis have used a three-fold approach for decision-making. It was understood that one had to consider how things were dealt with in the past, identify all present issues, and think about how those choices would impact future generations. This story is told in a three-fold manner covering three generations of Métis lived experience.

In regards to thinking about the future, the traditional teaching is that individuals must consider the impact of their choices upon seven future generations. The seven generations thinking approach creates a great emphasis on making responsible choices in all matters. Seven generations thinking is applied everywhere from individual choices, family decisions, community-based issues, Métis Nation considerations, and how to relate to the rest of creation. The infinity symbol always reminds Métis people to practice all these teachings in all of our daily affairs so that we can maintain a balanced life.

Leah Dorion, originally from Prince Albert, Saskatchewan, is a Métis artist, author, curriculum developer, lecturer, and researcher. She has taught Métis History and Native Studies for the First Nations University of Canada, the Gabriel Dumont Institute (GDI), and the University of Saskatchewan. For eight years, she was employed in GDI's Publishing Department: first as a Curriculum Developer and later as a Publishing Coordinator. She has authored or contributed to numerous books including *The Snow Tunnel Sisters*, *Metis Legacy* I and II, and *Drops of Brandy*. Leah is a visual artist, and an instructor at the Saskatchewan Urban Native Teacher Education Program in Prince Albert. She recently completed her Master of Arts in Integrated Studies from Athabasca University. For more information about her artistic vision and some of her current creative projects, visit her website at **www.leahdorion.com**.

Norman Fleury, originally from St. Lazare, Manitoba, is a gifted Michif storyteller. He speaks Michif-Cree, Cree, Ojibway, Dakota, French, and English. Tireless in the promotion and preservation of Michif, he has contributed to dozens of language resources including a dictionary, grammar books, and has provided innumerable translations for cultural resources. Norman has been employed as a life skills trainer, a university coordinator, a corrections worker, a group home worker, and has served as the executive director of the Brandon Indian and Métis Friendship Centre, and was the Manitoba Métis Federation's Michif Language Program Director. He presently farms near Woodnorth, Manitoba, and serves as an Elder for Brandon University.

Leah Dorion, originally from Prince Albert, Saskatchewan, is a Métis artist, author, curriculum developer, lecturer, and researcher. She has taught Métis History and Native Studies for the First Nations University of Canada, the Gabriel Dumont Institute (GDI), and the University of Saskatchewan. For eight years, she was employed in GDI's Publishing Department: first as a Curriculum Developer and later as a Publishing Coordinator. She has authored or contributed to numerous books including *The Snow Tunnel Sisters*, *Metis Legacy* I and II, and *Drops of Brandy*. Leah is a visual artist, and an instructor at the Saskatchewan Urban Native Teacher Education Program in Prince Albert. She recently completed her Master of Arts in Integrated Studies from Athabasca University. For more information about her artistic vision and some of her current creative projects, visit her website at **www.leahdorion.com**.

Norman Fleury, originally from St. Lazare, Manitoba, is a gifted Michif storyteller. He speaks Michif-Cree, Cree, Ojibway, Dakota, French, and English. Tireless in the promotion and preservation of Michif, he has contributed to dozens of language resources including a dictionary, grammar books, and has provided innumerable translations for cultural resources. Norman has been employed as a life skills trainer, a university coordinator, a corrections worker, a group home worker, and has served as the executive director of the Brandon Indian and Métis Friendship Centre, and was the Manitoba Métis Federation's Michif Language Program Director. He presently farms near Woodnorth, Manitoba, and serves as an Elder for Brandon University.

Leah Dorion, originally from Prince Albert, Saskatchewan, is a Métis artist, author, curriculum developer, lecturer, and researcher. She has taught Métis History and Native Studies for the First Nations University of Canada, the Gabriel Dumont Institute (GDI), and the University of Saskatchewan. For eight years, she was employed in GDI's Publishing Department: first as a Curriculum Developer and later as a Publishing Coordinator. She has authored or contributed to numerous books including *The Snow Tunnel Sisters*, *Metis Legacy* I and II, and *Drops of Brandy*. Leah is a visual artist, and an instructor at the Saskatchewan Urban Native Teacher Education Program in Prince Albert. She recently completed her Master of Arts in Integrated Studies from Athabasca University. For more information about her artistic vision and some of her current creative projects, visit her website at **www.leahdorion.com**.

Norman Fleury, originally from St. Lazare, Manitoba, is a gifted Michif storyteller. He speaks Michif-Cree, Cree, Ojibway, Dakota, French, and English. Tireless in the promotion and preservation of Michif, he has contributed to dozens of language resources including a dictionary, grammar books, and has provided innumerable translations for cultural resources. Norman has been employed as a life skills trainer, a university coordinator, a corrections worker, a group home worker, and has served as the executive director of the Brandon Indian and Métis Friendship Centre, and was the Manitoba Métis Federation's Michif Language Program Director. He presently farms near Woodnorth, Manitoba, and serves as an Elder for Brandon University.

Leah Dorion, originally from Prince Albert, Saskatchewan, is a Métis artist, author, curriculum developer, lecturer, and researcher. She has taught Métis History and Native Studies for the First Nations University of Canada, the Gabriel Dumont Institute (GDI), and the University of Saskatchewan. For eight years, she was employed in GDI's Publishing Department: first as a Curriculum Developer and later as a Publishing Coordinator. She has authored or contributed to numerous books including *The Snow Tunnel Sisters*, *Metis Legacy* I and II, and *Drops of Brandy*. Leah is a visual artist, and an instructor at the Saskatchewan Urban Native Teacher Education Program in Prince Albert. She recently completed her Master of Arts in Integrated Studies from Athabasca University. For more information about her artistic vision and some of her current creative projects, visit her website at **www.leahdorion.com**.

Norman Fleury, originally from St. Lazare, Manitoba, is a gifted Michif storyteller. He speaks Michif-Cree, Cree, Ojibway, Dakota, French, and English. Tireless in the promotion and preservation of Michif, he has contributed to dozens of language resources including a dictionary, grammar books, and has provided innumerable translations for cultural resources. Norman has been employed as a life skills trainer, a university coordinator, a corrections worker, a group home worker, and has served as the executive director of the Brandon Indian and Métis Friendship Centre, and was the Manitoba Métis Federation's Michif Language Program Director. He presently farms near Woodnorth, Manitoba, and serves as an Elder for Brandon University.